Playalong Showtu

Fingering Chart 3

Performance Tips 6

All I Ask Of You *from* **The Phantom Of The Opera** 14

Cabaret *from* **Cabaret** 11

Can't Help Lovin' Dat Man *from* **Showboat** 16

Don't Cry For Me Argentina *from* **Evita** 18

I Dreamed A Dream *from* **Les Misérables** 22

Hopelessly Devoted To You *from* **Grease** 20

Mamma Mia *from* **Mamma Mia!** 24

Some Enchanted Evening *from* **South Pacific** 26

Take That Look Off Your Face *from* **Tell Me On A Sunday** 28

Tell Me It's Not True *from* **Blood Brothers** 30

Wise Publications
part of The Music Sales Group
London/New York/Paris/Sydney/Copenhagen/Berlin/Madrid/Tokyo

Published by
Wise Publications
14-15 Berners Street, London W1T 3LJ, UK.

Exclusive Distributors:
Music Sales Limited
Distribution Centre, Newmarket Road, Bury St Edmunds, Suffolk IP33 3YB, UK.
Music Sales Pty Limited
120 Rothschild Avenue, Rosebery, NSW 2018, Australia.

Order No. AM986062
ISBN 1-84609-611-1
This book © Copyright 2006 Wise Publications,
a division of Music Sales Limited.

Arranging and engraving supplied by Camden Music.
Compiled by Heather Slater.
Cover design by Chloe Alexander.
Printed in the EU.

CD recorded, mixed and mastered by John Rose and Jonas Persson.
Instrumental solos by Jamie Talbot.
New backing tracks arranged by Paul Honey.
Melody line arrangements by Christopher Hussey.

Your Guarantee of Quality
As publishers, we strive to produce every book to the highest commercial standards.
The music has been freshly engraved and the book has been carefully designed to minimise
awkward page turns and to make playing from it a real pleasure.
Particular care has been given to specifying acid-free, neutral-sized paper made from pulps
which have not been elemental chlorine bleached. This pulp is from farmed sustainable forests
and was produced with special regard for the environment.
Throughout, the printing and binding have been planned to ensure a sturdy, attractive
publication which should give years of enjoyment.
If your copy fails to meet our high standards, please inform us and we will gladly replace it.

www.musicsales.com

FREE bonus material downloadable to your computer.
Visit: www.hybridpublications.com
Registration is free and easy.
Your registration code is: RK398

Can't Help Lovin' Dat Man
(from 'Showboat')

Music by Jerome Kern

Don't Cry For Me Argentina
(from 'Evita')

Music by Andrew Lloyd Webber

Hopelessly Devoted To You
(from 'Grease')

Music by John Farrar

I Dreamed A Dream
(from 'Les Misérables')

Music by Claude-Michel Schönberg

Mamma Mia
(from 'Mamma Mia!')

Words & Music by Benny Andersson, Stig Anderson & Björn Ulvaeus

Some Enchanted Evening
(from 'South Pacific')

Music by Richard Rodgers

molto rit.

cresc.

1:45

a tempo

mf

poco rit.   **a tempo**

cresc.

poco rit.

f

2:23

a tempo

mp   *p*

molto rit.   **Very slowly**

mp   *p*

Take That Look Off Your Face
(from 'Tell Me On A Sunday')

Music by Andrew Lloyd Webber

With a driving rhythm ♩ = 110

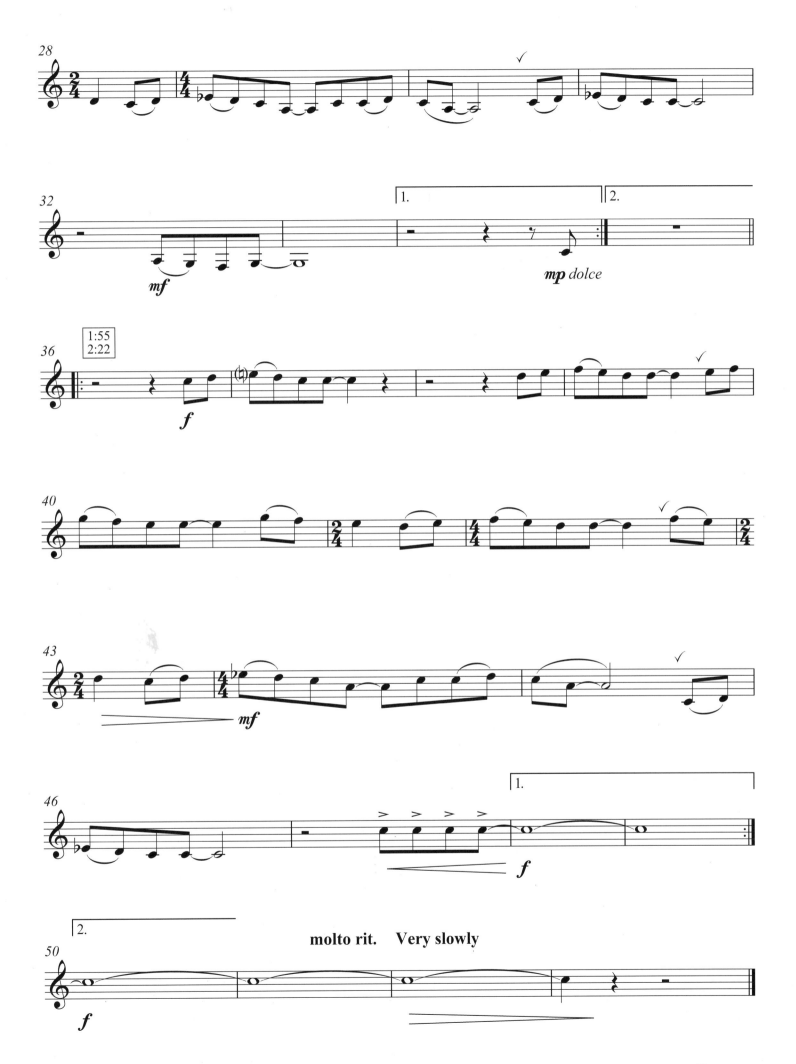

Tell Me It's Not True
(from 'Blood Brothers')

Music by Willy Russell

Steadily ♩ = 74

(piano)

molto rit.

1 2 3 4 5 6 7 8 9

CD Track Listing

1   Tuning notes

Full instrumental performances...

2   Cabaret *from* **Cabaret**
(Ebb/Kander) Carlin Music Corporation

3   All I Ask Of You *from* **The Phantom Of The Opera**
(Lloyd Webber/Hart) The Really Useful Group

4   Can't Help Lovin' Dat Man *from* **Showboat**
(Hammerstein/Kern) Universal Music Publishing Limited/Chappell Music Limited

5   Don't Cry For Me Argentina *from* **Evita**
(Lloyd Webber/Rice) Evita Music Limitd

6   Hopelessly Devoted To You *from* **Grease**
(Farrar) Famous Music Publishing Limited

7   I Dreamed A Dream *from* **Les Misérables**
(Schönberg/Boublil/Natel/Kretzmer) Alain Boublil Music Overseas Limited

8   Mamma Mia *from* **Mammia Mia!**
(Andersson/Anderson/Ulvaeus) Bocu Music Limited

9   Some Enchanted Evening *from* **South Pacific**
(Hammerstein/Rodgers) EMI Music Publishing Limited

10   Take That Look Off Your Face *from* **Tell Me On A Sunday**
(Lloyd Webber/Black) The Really Useful Group Limited

11   Tell Me It's Not True *from* **Blood Brothers**
(Russell) Timeact Limited

Backing tracks only...

12 Cabaret *from* **Cabaret**
13 All I Ask Of You *from* **The Phantom Of The Opera**
14 Can't Help Lovin' Dat Man *from* **Showboat**
15 Don't Cry For Me Argentina *from* **Evita**
16 Hopelessly Devoted To You *from* **Grease**
17 I Dreamed A Dream *from* **Les Misérables**
18 Mamma Mia *from* **Mamma Mia!**
19 Some Enchanted Evening *from* **South Pacific**
20 Take That Look Off Your Face *from* **Tell Me On A Sunday**
21 Tell Me It's Not True *from* **Blood Brothers**

To remove your CD from the plastic sleeve, lift the small lip to break the perforations. Replace the disc after use for convenient storage.